This Little Hippo
book belongs to

**For JoAnna and Hannah.**
**S.H.**

Scholastic Children's Books,
Commonwealth House, 1 – 19 New Oxford Street,
London WC1A 1NU
a division of Scholastic Ltd

London • New York • Toronto • Sydney • Auckland

First published in the UK by Little Hippo,
an imprint of Scholastic Ltd

Copyright © Scholastic Ltd 1997
Illustrations copyright © Sue Heap 1997

All rights reserved

ISBN  0 590 19651 0

Printed and bound in China

2 4 6 8 10 9 7 5 3 1

The right of Sue Heap to be identified as the illustrator
of this work has been asserted by her in accordance
with the Copyright, Designs and Patents Act, 1988.

# BUSY AS A BEE

## Sue Heap

Little
Hippo

# slow
# bear

fast
hare

small
snail

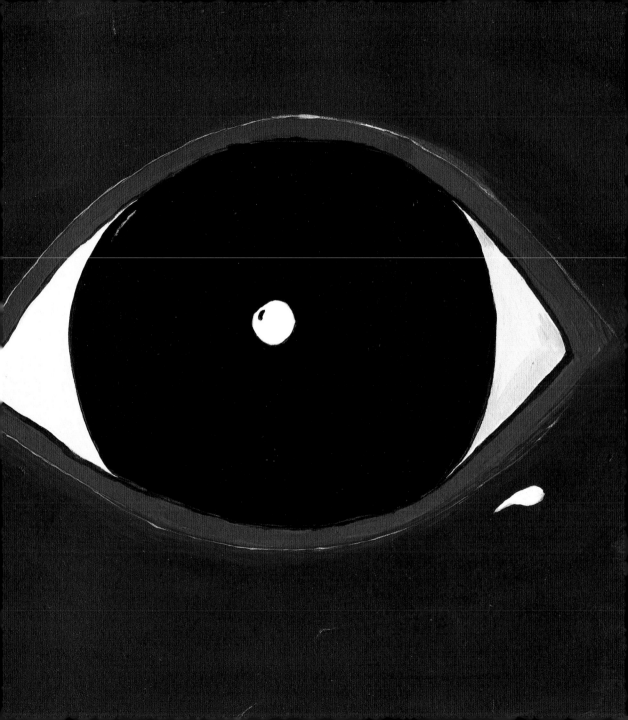

**big
whale**

# quiet
# dog

**noisy frog**

**wet
moose**

**dry**
**goose**

# lazy
# fleas

**busy bees**